CALAMITY JANE

A MUSICAL WESTERN

adapted by

RONALD HANMER *and* PHIL PARK

from

the stage play

by

CHARLES K. FREEMAN

after

The WARNER BROS. Film

written by

JAMES O'HANLON

Lyrics
by
PAUL FRANCIS WEBSTER

Music
by
SAMMY FAIN

Vocal Score

WARNER CHAPPELL MUSIC LTD., 129 Park Street, London W1Y 3FA

Licensed for performance by

JOSEF WEINBERGER LTD.,

10-16 Rathbone Street,
London, W1P 2BJ

By arrangement with Tams-Witmark Music Library, New York City.

CALAMITY JANE

CHARACTERS

CALAMITY JANE — *The hard-bitten, gun-totin' heroine, who tries to behave like a man but can't help loving like a woman*

WILD BILL HICKOCK — *Handsome, professional gambler, about 35*

LIEUT. DANNY GILMARTIN — *Good-looking young officer*

KATIE BROWN — *Attractive stage-struck young lady from the Big City*

HENRY MILLER — *Proprietor of " The Golden Garter "*

SUSAN — *Miller's pretty young niece*

FRANCIS FRYER — *A song-and-dance man*

ADELAIDE ADAMS — *A show-business star*

RATTLESNAKE — *An old stage-coach driver*

" DOC " PIERCE — *Deadwood's doctor-undertaker*

JOE — *Bartender at " The Golden Garter "*

HANK ⎱
PETE ⎰ — *Two Scouts*

THE COLONEL OF FORT SCULLY

COWPUNCHERS, BULLWHACKERS, PROSPECTORS, TRAPPERS, INDIANS, WOMEN OF THE TOWN, CHORUS-GIRLS, OFFICERS, SOLDIERS and their WIVES, STAGE-COACH PASSENGERS, ETC.

SYNOPSIS OF SCENES

ACT ONE

SCENE 1 " THE GOLDEN GARTER ", Deadwood City, Dakota Territory
SCENE 2 THE STAR DRESSING-ROOM, Bijou Theatre, Chicago
SCENE 3 " THE GOLDEN GARTER " again

ACT TWO

SCENE 1 CALAMITY JANE'S CABIN
SCENE 2 A TRAIL, through a Pass in the Black Hills
SCENE 3 FORT SCULLY
SCENE 4 THE TRAIL again
SCENE 5 " THE GOLDEN GARTER "

Time : 1876

CALAMITY JANE

NOTES ON PRINCIPAL CHARACTERS

CALAMITY JANE—In order to hold her own in a man's world, she dresses, speaks, rides and shoots like a man ; groomed and dressed in proper feminine fashion, she is revealed as a beautiful girl—and the transformation is quite startling.

WILD BILL HICKOCK—Aged about 35, and a handsome figure of a man, he is an ex-peace-officer turned professional gambler. Good-natured, with a sense of humour. In love with Calamity Jane, but doesn't know it.

LIEUT. DANNY GILMARTIN—A young officer attached to the nearby fort. He is the man Calamity Jane dreams about, but he falls in love with somebody quite different.

KATIE BROWN—A stage-struck city-girl who poses as a famous actress, but has good looks and talents of her own.

HENRY MILLER—Proprietor of "The Golden Garter" Deadwood City's saloon-hotel-theatre. Aged about 50, he is nervous and erratic, giving the impression he is constantly only one jump ahead of a nervous breakdown. (Non-Singing)

SUSAN—Miller's young, friendly and pretty niece. (Non-Singing).

FRANCIS FRYER—A song-and-dance man more at home in the vaudeville theatres of the Eastern States than in the Wild West.

ADELAIDE ADAMS—A highly-paid vaudeville star and celebrated " beauty " of the period : off-stage, a selfish and conceited woman.

RATTLESNAKE—A bewhiskered old fossil who drives the stage-coach. (Non-Singing).

" DOC " PIERCE—Deadwood City's doctor-under-taker, with doubtful qualifications but considerable experience. A poker-playing pal of Hickock's. (Non-Singing).

JOE—Bartender at " The Golden Garter ". (Non-Singing).

THE ORCHESTRA

The complete orchestra for " Calamity Jane " comprises, 3 Trumpets, 2 Trombones, 4 Saxes, Horn, Violins A. B. C., Viola, Cello, Bass, Guitar, Drums and Piano. The 1st Alto, 2nd Alto and 2nd Tenor Saxes double Clarinet; the 1st Tenor Sax doubles Flute. However, in the event of Saxes not being available, parts are provided for non-doubling Flute and 1st and 2nd Clarinets. A 3rd Clarinet may be added by playing the whole of the 2nd Tenor Sax part on Clarinet. A special orchestral piano part is supplied, which should be used ; the pianist should NOT use the vocal score. The Violin parts are printed Violin A to one book ; Violin B and C together in a second book.

The minimum combination for a successful performance is 2 Trumpets, 1 Trombone, 3 Saxes (or 3 Wood-wind), 3 Violins, Cello, Bass, Drums and Piano. Thereafter, instruments should be added in the following order ; 2nd Trombone, 2nd Tenor Sax (or 3rd Clarinet), 3rd Trumpet, additional Violins, Viola, Horn and Guitar.

All parts are cued where necessary, and the vocal score has complete instrumental marks and cues for the conductors' guidance.

RONALD HANMER

CALAMITY JANE

MUSICAL NUMBERS

CALAMITY JANE

Lyrics by
PAUL FRANCIS WEBSTER

Music by
SAMMY FAIN
Music adapted
and arranged by
RONALD HANMER

OVERTURE

4

ACT I

THE DEADWOOD STAGE

(CALAMITY and ENSEMBLE)

Bright 2 ($\text{♩}=108$)

Cho. Whip crack a-way, whip crack a-way, whip crack a-way!

Cho. Here they be! Here they be! How's a-bout a wel-come? A peace-ful sort of welcome for the

Cho. gang! Bang! Oh, the Deadwood stage is finall-y home a - gain!

CALAMITY JANE enters followed by RATTLESNAKE and passengers from the stage-coach

18

CARELESS WITH THE TRUTH
(CALAMITY, BILL & MEN)

Cue: CALAMITY: You callin' me a liar again Bill Hickock?
AD LIBS: Tell us another etc.

24

26

Bill: not ex-act-ly ly-in', but she's care-less with the truth!____

Men: not ex-act-ly ly-in', but she's care-less with the truth!

Tutti

8 **Andante misterioso** (♩ = 88)
Stgs. Cls.

p Tom. Cello. Bass.

9 **Bright 2** (♩ = 100)
CALAMITY

Cal. Did I tell ya 'bout the time last fall, I'm log-gin' trees at Lake St. Paul; And there I see an

p Stgs pizz Clars
w.w.
mp Brass

Cal. oak so tall, t'would take a bird a day to reach the top._____ Well,

Brass

28

3

ADELAIDE
(BILL & MEN)

Cue: BILL: You see her carved on the prow of an ancient ship....
.... in a gambler's cameo....
in the dyin' embers of a campfire ....

Moderato in 4 (♩=122)

32

EV'RYONE COMPLAINS ABOUT THE WEATHER
(FRYER)

Cue: FRYER: But you can at least let me *show* you! . .

Nº 5

MEN!

Cue: BILL: "Like a touchy old woman"....
H'm... Maybe he's got something there....
CALAMITY: Why, you...you...!
(She reaches for something to throw at him)
Men...!

Bright Waltz (♩.=60)

CALAMITY

Men! Men! Hor-ri-ble men! I've said it be-fore and I'll say it a-

-gain, what I think of men you can't print in a book_____ Luck-y the girl who has

ne- - -ver been took!_____ Men!

Cal. Males! Males! Rip-roar-in' males!

Cal. Fris-ky from whis-key and fill-in' up jails, A five dol-lar wa-ger, will get you a

Cal. ten___ no Deadwood coy-o-te will hog - - tie this hen!___ Men are

Cal. made to breed con-fu-sion;___ love is wois'-n a pois-on-ous bite

Cal. ___ so I've come to this con-clu-sion___ I don't want an-y part of 'em

Nº 6

CAN - CAN

Cue: MILLER: .... the Golden Garter Show!

HIVE FULL OF HONEY

(FRYER)

Cue; MILLER: . . . the toast of New York. . . . Miss Frances Fryer!

(FRYER *enters*) **Moderate 4 (♩=112)**

Tpt. Solo

FRYER: (*In high-pitched girls falsetto*)

I've got two wonderful arms, I've got two wonderful lips, I'm ov-er

Vlns. W.W.

Fry. twen-ty one__ and I'm free_____ Oh, I've got a hive full of hon-ey For the

Fry. right kind of hon-ey bee!__ I'm not the glam-or-ous type, but I'm the

I CAN DO WITHOUT YOU

(CALAMITY and BILL)

Cue: CALAMITY; ain't nuthin' you say means any thing to me! . . . .

54

SEGUE Nº 9

OPENING SCENE II

№ 10

"IT'S HARRY I'M PLANNING TO MARRY"

(ADELAIDE and the JOHNNIES)

Cue: ADELAIDE: . . . . my farewell performance!

58

№ 10a   REPRISE: "IT'S HARRY I'M PLANNING TO MARRY"

(KATIE)

Cue: KATIE *strikes an 'Adelaide Adams' pose in front of mirror.*

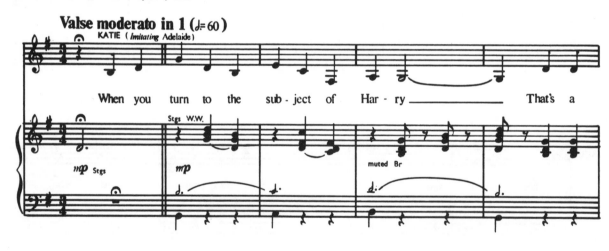

61

Nº 11

OPENING SCENE III
Reprise: ADELAIDE
(MEN)

Cue CALAMITY: . . . somebody's being hustled. *(Black-out)*

NOTE: If shorter scene-change music is required, the first repeat may be omitted, or a start made at either 1 or 2

3 Moderato (♩ = 108)

Hn. Saxes.

CURTAIN

Vlns.

mf Saxes.

SOLO TENOR **Slowly and sadly** **4**

If you give a man a wish, ten to one he would wish for that one per-fect girl, Ad-e-

MEN

Mm_____ Mm Mm_____

4

p Stgs.

66

Nº 12

WINDY CITY
(CALAMITY & CHORUS)

Cue: CALAMITY: . . . . the biggest noise in Illinois!

№ 13

KEEP IT UNDER YOUR HAT
(KATIE)

Cue: MILLER: . . . . the one and only Adelaide Adams!

Kate. in the can;— So if you wanna know the way to keep your man,— Keep it un-der your

Kate. hat, Hat-tie, Keep it under your hat, Hat-tie, Keep it under your hat!

№ 14   REPRISE: KEEP IT UNDER YOUR HAT
(KATIE & CHORUS)

Cue: KATIE: My own way? Okay — I will!

Moderato 4 (♩ =120)

KATIE *(with style & confidence)*

Kate. Well, now if you've got a cu-tie Who's a real sweet patootie, Better

Kate keep it un-der your hat— Just re-member cu-ri-os-i-ty, in fa-bles of old—

80

Kate: killed the cur - i - ous cat __ Supposin' you love a laddie Who's a real sug - ar dad-dy, Better

Kate: take in the welcoming mat; __ Re - member there's a dozen dolls for ev - 'ry Dan __ You're

Kate: not the on - ly sweet pea in the can So if you wanna know the way to keep your man __

Kate: Keep it un-der your hat, Hat - tie, Keep it un-der your hat, Hat - tie,

Kate: Keep it un-der your hat! Well, now if you've got a cu-tie who's a real sweet patoo-tie, Better

GIRLS: Well, now if you've got a cu-tie who's a real sweet patoo-tie, Better

BOYS: Well, now if you've got a cu-tie who's a real sweet patoo-tie, Better

82

№ 15

FINALE ACT I
REPRISE : CARELESS WITH THE TRUTH
(ENSEMBLE & CHORUS)

Cue: CALAMITY: . . . .the only girl for the Golden Garter was *Katie Brown!*
(*Big laugh from everybody*)

END OF ACT I

Nº 16

ENTR'ACTE

ACT II
OPENING ACT II
A WOMAN'S TOUCH
(CALAMITY & KATIE)

№ 17

96

HIGHER THAN A HAWK
(BILL)

Cue: **BILL** : *(looking at photo)* What a gal . . . .

BLACK HILLS OF DAKOTA
(CHORUS)

Cue: CALAMITY *swoons into* BILL'S *arms. Blackout. Tabs.*

Cho. love!_____ So take me, Take me back to the Black Hills, The

Cho Black Hills of Da - ko - ta____ To the beau-ti-ful In-di-an coun-try that I love. Black

Cho Hills, I love! love! love!_____

Segue, after applause

Nº 19a

OPENING SCENE III
REPRISE: BLACK HILLS OF DAKOTA
(CALAMITY, KATIE, BILL, DANNY & CHORUS.)

Black Hills of Da-ko-ta To the beau-ti-ful In-di-an coun-try that I

Black Hills of Da-ko-ta To the beau-ti-ful In-di-an coun-try that I

Ah _____ Ah _____ coun-try that I

love _____

love _____

love _____

6 **Tempo di Polka** *exeunt* PRINCIPALS

6 **Tempo di Polka** CURTAIN Stgs W.W.

Tutti *pp cresc molto* *ff* *sffz f*

7

8 COLONEL: Nice to see you all — very

good of you to come! I hope you all have a very enjoyable evening! GUESTS: We will! etc.

9 *Enter KATIE and DANNY, followed by CALAMITY and BILL.*

Music continues and fades under ensuing dialogue and action. **10**

Nº 20

Cue: **DANNY**: Calamity can be your bridesmaid. . . .

LOVE YOU DEARLY
(KATIE & DANNY)

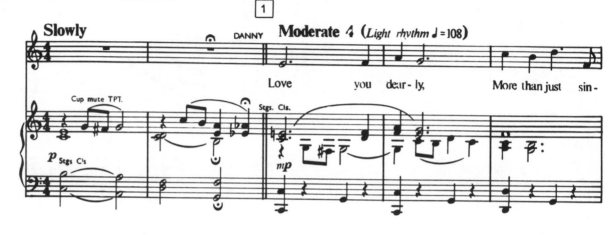

Love you dear - ly, More than just sin-

-cere-ly, More than I could ev-er hope to say;

Love you dear-ly, words can't ex-press it clear-ly You seem to take my

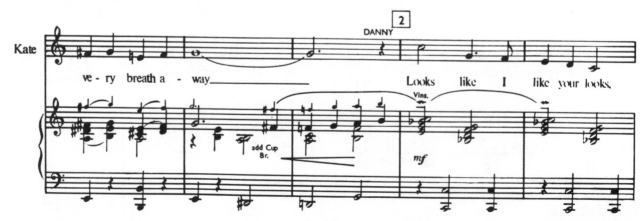

ve-ry breath a - way_____ Looks like I like your looks,

FINALETTO
(CALAMITY & BILL)

Cue: BILL: . . . .disrupt the whole fort if they see ya like that ! (*Exit*)

118

119

120

the way....   BILL: I'm takin' you home whether you   CALAMITY: Now see here, Bill
                like it or not - so c'mon -   Hickock -

BILL: For Pete's   sake let's get goin .....   If   anyone   catches you   an'   me this way,   Deadwood   City'll   never

be the same again!   **6**   *Exeunt. CURTAIN*

№ 22   OPENING SCENE IV

Broadly (♩ = 80)

CURTAIN UP *Enter* CALAMITY *and* BILL

Fl. Vlns.

Alto Sax(or Cl.)

Fade out on dialogue

Vln

rit

№ 23

MY SECRET LOVE
(CALAMITY)

Cue: BILL: You'll get over Danny, too....

Cal.

Ev - en told the gol-den daf - fo - dils! At last my heart's an op-en

Moderate rhythm

Cal

door,_____ And my secret love's no secret, an - y more._____

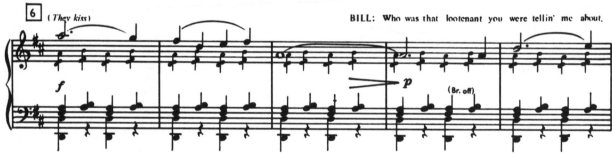

6 (*They kiss*)

BILL: Who was that lootenant you were tellin' me about,

a while back? CALAMITY: Never heard of 'im... BILL: What you say to us takin' a ride just the two of us?

We could watch the moon hangin' high over the mountains.... CALAMITY: The way it'll look, I shan't ever have seen it before....

№ 23a   MELOS AND REPRISE: MY SECRET LOVE
(CALAMITY & BILL)

Cue: DANNY: This note she left me says everything. Listen. . . .

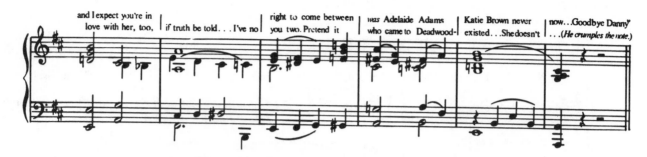

BILL   "Never existed" .... She was the most *real* person in Deadwood.

CALAMITY   *(with sudden resolution)* I've gotta bring her back .... There's nothin' else for it— I've gotta bring her back!

DANNY   But she's on her way to Valley Falls –

CALAMITY   But she ain't gonna catch no stage – not while I can ride faster'n any woman alive!   I'm gittin' back to the cabin, quick! Bill, you can saddle up fer me, while I get m'deerskins on .... While I'm gone, find a preacher to do the splicin'! .... Danny, you git back to the Fort an' invite the folks to a weddin'– a *double* weddin'– you and Katie, 'n me and Bill.

DANNY   *(after a stunned pause)* Did– did you say you –and--- Bill?

CALAMITY   That's right!

BILL   Sure is.

DANNY   Well I'll be! .... Bill, I don't know what kind of a life you'll have with this catamount, ...

Nᵒ 24

REPRISE: WINDY CITY
(CHORUS)

Just blew in from the Win-dy Ci-ty, The Win-dy Ci-ty is migh-ty pretty, But they aint got what

Cho. we got, No, sir - ree! They got shacks up to sev-en storeys, They ne-ver see an-y

Cho. morning glories, But a step from our door - way We got 'em for free!

They got those

Cho. Pret - ty la-dies in their big chapeaux.

minstrel shows Private lawns, public parks, Ah

For the sake of

№ 25

FINALE
(FULL COMPANY)

Cue: RATTLESNAKE: Deadwood Stage all ready fer the weddin' party!

CHORUS: Oh, the Deadwood stage is a-rol-lin' on ov-er the plains_____

Cho. _____ With the cur-tains flappin' and the driver a-slappin' the reins_____

Cho. Beauti-ful sky_____ A won-der-ful day_____ Whip crack a-way, whip

138

142

CURTAIN CALL
(THE BLACK HILLS OF DAKOTA)

146

PLAY - OUT